A Look at
Cross-Addiction

About the pamphlet
Cross-addiction is a transfer of addictions, the exchange of one harmful dependency for another. What happens when someone substitutes one addictive substance or behavior for another? He or she runs the risk of developing a new addiction, returning to the original one, or both.

Living with an addiction can be tough; living with two or more can seem hopeless. There is hope, however, and reading *A Look at Cross-Addiction*—or rereading it—is a wise step at any stage of recovery. This pamphlet explains what cross-addiction is and the forms it can take, how to begin recovering from it, and how to avoid it in the future.

About the author
Saul Selby has worked professionally in the field of addiction since 1983. He was previously a clinical director at Hazelden Foundation and is currently the president of Set-Free Recovery Services. Author and therapist, he speaks nationally on topics related to addiction, mental health, and spirituality.

Hazelden Classics for Continuing Care

A Look at Cross-Addiction

Revised Edition

Saul Selby

Hazelden
Publishing

Hazelden Publishing
Center City, Minnesota 55012-0176

hazelden.org/bookstore
800-328-9000

ISBN: 978-0-89486-331-8

The Twelve Steps of AA are reprinted with permission of Alcoholics Anonymous World Services, Inc. Permission to reprint the Twelve Steps does not mean that Alcoholics Anonymous has reviewed or approved the contents of this publication, nor that AA agrees with the views expressed herein. The views expressed herein are solely those of the author. AA is a program of recovery from alcoholism. Use of the Twelve Steps in connection with programs and activities that are patterned after AA, but which address other problems, does not imply otherwise.

The names of the people in this pamphlet who have shared their experiences have been changed. This pamphlet also includes some experiences that are composites taken from a group of people who have had similar experiences. In the last case, any resemblance to specific people or specific situations is accidental.

Cover and interior design by David Spohn
Typesetting by Tursso Companies

INTRODUCTION

Waking from a fitful sleep, Sandra couldn't believe her eyes—or her head, for that matter. She had a pounding headache and felt nauseated, but that wasn't the worst of it. As her blurred vision began to clear, she slowly started to realize where she was. The setting was familiar, but it wasn't her bedroom. It was the county detox center. Feelings of anger, depression, and self-disgust flooded her. *Not again,* she thought. *I swore to my husband and kids six months ago that I'd never drink again. How could this have happened?*

Why do people relapse? Why do people like Sandra who seem so sincere in their commitment to recovery go back to drinking and using? This question has puzzled thousands of members of Twelve Step programs and other recovery groups. While the reasons people relapse are not always clear, one reason frequently stands out: they didn't understand cross-addiction. This pamphlet's purpose is to help the reader understand cross-addiction in order to attain balance in recovery and avoid a possible relapse.

WHAT IS CROSS-ADDICTION?

Cross-addiction is simply a transfer of addictions, the exchange of one harmful dependency for another. Substituting one mood-altering drug for another is perhaps the most common form of cross-addiction. Valium for alcohol, alcohol for heroin, and marijuana for cocaine are just some examples. The list goes on and on, but the result is always the same—disaster. The decision to switch from one chemical to another has shipwrecked thousands of individuals' efforts to recover. Sincere and hopeful people who are trying to overcome an addiction fall victim to the lure of cross-addiction. They don't foresee the impending danger. Danger? What danger? Why is it harmful for a recovering alcoholic to smoke a little pot, or a recovering cocaine addict to drink a glass of wine with dinner, or an ex-junkie to use some

1

Valium to calm down? These are fair questions and are asked by many in early recovery. *I have used these chemicals before,* they reason, *and they never caused me any problems.* This reasoning may seem sound on the surface, but it's not. It's a deceptive first step on the road back to addiction.

What really happens when an addict exchanges one mood-altering chemical for another? The first predictable outcome is a new addiction: the addict becomes addicted to the substitute chemical. This may not happen immediately. It may take months or even years. The intention, stated or otherwise, is to use the new chemical in moderation. Just a little, mind you, not enough to cause any problems—and just for a little while. But the addict eventually uses more and more, the problems get worse and worse, and the addict is right back where he or she started. The addict now has the same problem, but a new master. The new master may be called alcohol instead of heroin, or marijuana instead of Valium. But it doesn't matter. Whatever the new master's name, the addict's reality is still the same: enslavement. For the chemically dependent person, substituting one chemical for another makes about as much sense as changing rooms on the Titanic.

But that's not all. A new addiction isn't the only danger associated with trading one chemical for another. Using a substitute chemical often results in a return to the chemical of choice. Why? Because the resolve to abstain from the drug of choice weakens when another mood-altering chemical is being used. Clouded judgment is a natural by-product of drug use, and the new chemical convinces the addict that the old chemical wasn't really that bad. The pain and problems associated with the drug of choice are quickly ignored, so it seems reasonable to use it again. The new result is that the addict falls prey to two or more mood-altering drugs instead of one. The following three stories make all too clear the dangers of replacing one chemical with another.

Alcohol for Cocaine

Janet slowly became aware that she was losing control of her cocaine use. What at first was periodic use soon grew into an expensive habit. Aside from the expense, her cocaine use caused problems at work and hurt her relationship with her fiancé. As she looked closely at the problems in her life, she vowed, *I will never use cocaine again.* However, she gave herself permission to drink alcohol. *Alcohol is legal*, she rationalized, *and it never caused me the problems cocaine did.* Janet was in for a surprise. Within two months, the amount and frequency of her drinking had tripled. With the increasing drinking came many more problems, including the end of her relationship with her fiancé. It became painfully clear that cocaine was not her problem, *chemical use* was.

Valium for Pot

For years, Bill had smoked pot as a way to relieve stress. Every day after work, Bill would go home and smoke two or three joints to settle his nerves. *This is the life*, he thought, as he sat in his favorite chair, turned on the TV, and lit up a joint. But his family and the legal system felt differently. His wife and kids complained that he was "zoned out" all the time. Their complaints didn't faze Bill. *They just don't realize how stressful my life is*, he told himself, and continued to smoke pot, feeling no guilt. But after Bill's second DUI, the local judge helped him see the light. After being court-ordered into treatment for chemical dependency, Bill realized he needed to stop smoking pot. But he needed a new way to relieve stress. Soon after leaving treatment, he talked a physician into giving him Valium. Within six months, he not only had worked his way up to three times the recommended dose of Valium, but also had returned to smoking pot.

Codeine for Alcohol

David, a recovering alcoholic, was proud of his eight years of sobriety. After an accident at work, he was forced to seek medical attention for a back injury. His doctor, who was aware of his alcoholism, recommended a form of therapy for his pain that did not include mood-altering drugs. But David was not satisfied. He sought the advice of two other physicians, and one of them gave him a prescription for codeine. David had been warned about the potential dangers of taking painkillers but felt confident he could handle the risk. *After all, I've been sober eight years*, he reasoned. So he began to medicate himself. At first he used the codeine as prescribed; then he began to abuse it. Finally, he started drinking again.

Janet, Bill, and David are just three of thousands of chemically dependent people who have learned about cross-addiction the hard way, through the pain of personal experience. For these three people, complete abstinence from all mood-altering chemicals is the only answer. And their stories are not unique—this same principle applies to all of us who are chemically dependent. We cannot safely use any mood-altering chemicals. Moderate use of any addictive substances is simply not an option. The question is, do we believe this? Will we accept this reality? Will we learn from the experiences of others like Janet, Bill, and David, or will we learn the *hard* way, the *painful* way—by *personal experience*?

CROSS-ADDICTION AND DENIAL

Total abstinence is difficult for most addicts to accept. *Giving up all chemicals is unfair, unrealistic, and unnecessary*, we argue. We don't want to believe cross-addiction is real—because we're scared. The thought of facing life without chemicals is terrifying. It means experiencing ups and downs, fear, uncertainty, and—worst of all—pain, without an anesthetic. This is unacceptable to us, so we desperately try to find reasons, excuses, and rationalizations to *deny* our chemical dependency and our need for complete abstinence. Let's look at two of the most common excuses.

How Can Smoking a Little Pot Hurt?

Many addicts use their own "theory of relativity" to deny the need for complete abstinence—they consider some drugs harmful, and others safe. *The harmful ones must go*, they reason, *but the safe ones can stay*. How this is applied varies from person to person, depending on each one's experiences and preferences. Some might say, "I know I can't use cocaine, but marijuana is harmless," or "Heroin almost killed me, but codeine is safer," or "I can't seem to handle the hard liquor, but a little wine with dinner or a beer with the guys can't hurt."

Rationalization such as this is very common. What makes it particularly dangerous is the fact that there is often a shred of truth to it. The addict's experience may in fact support the idea that some drugs have been more harmful than others. And it is true that some drugs are legal and others illegal, and that some drugs may be physically addictive and others not. But these truths help blind us to the cross-addictive nature of our condition.

If My Doctor Prescribed It, It Must Be Okay

Here is another common and convincing rationalization used by many addicts: *It's all right because my doctor prescribed it*. Addicts mistakenly, or conveniently, choose to believe that any medications prescribed by a doctor can't harm them. We assume that doctors understand the potential dangers of drugs and would not prescribe anything harmful. Unfortunately, this is not always true. While most physicians are now sensitive to the problems of chemical addiction, some are not. Still others are targets for manipulative addicts who may lie to their physicians in order to obtain drugs. Many prescribed medications are *very* addictive and potentially dangerous for the recovering addict.

When dealing with physicians, remember that all mood-altering chemicals can lead to dependence and must be avoided if possible. If you are dependent, tell your physician that you need to avoid mood-altering chemicals. Ask if the drugs you are prescribed are mood-altering, and if so, ask if there are alternatives. If medical needs force you to use mood-altering chemicals, try not to administer them yourself. Family members or friends who can handle prescription drugs responsibly could give them to you. Remember, your abstinence is *your* responsibility. Don't assume the medical profession or anyone else understands your needs. Also, exercise caution when using over-the-counter medications, many of which contain alcohol, stimulants, or depressants and have the potential to become addictive.

HOW DOES CROSS-ADDICTION WORK?

Why is substituting one chemical for another a recipe for failure? This question can be answered by exploring the personality of the addict. Virtually all addicts share one common interest: they like to feel good. They would prefer, whenever possible, to avoid pain, discomfort, or anything that prevents them from feeling good all the time. Most addicts have a drug of choice, a favorite chemical that is the most satisfying, enjoyable, and pleasurable. The decision to abstain from the drug of choice is a great step in the recovery process, but it creates a new problem for the addict—reality. Without the drug of choice, this dependent person is no longer insulated from the pain and emotion of life and often experiences a great sense of emptiness, a void. This void, which was previously filled by the drug of choice, still insists it be satisfied in some way. *Fill me*, the void demands. To relieve the sense of emptiness, the addict will often make a deal with the void: *I can't give you your favorite drug, but let's try something else.*

The void within the addict will eventually demand complete satisfaction in order to avoid the pain, discomfort, and stresses life brings. In time, an addictive pattern similar or identical to the original pattern of chemical use develops. So the only practical strategy for the addict is complete abstinence from all mood-altering chemicals.

BEHAVIOR AND CROSS-ADDICTION

Addicts can attempt to satisfy the void in constructive or destructive ways. A particularly destructive tendency is to transfer the addiction from drugs to addictive behaviors—behaviors that on the surface may seem fine, acceptable, and even desirable. Just like the use of drugs, however, these behaviors may become obsessive and compulsive, causing problems for both the addict and his or her family. Let's explore the experiences of four people who got caught in this trap.

Sex

John felt relief when he completed his outpatient treatment program. He could now get back his driver's license and spend more time at home with his family. Though he was forced into treatment by the legal system, he was glad help was available. He knew drinking was killing him.

John was pretty honest about most things in treatment, except one—his sexual life. John had a long history of extramarital affairs and involvement with prostitutes. Ashamed of his actions, he chose not to say anything about them. He was concerned about his past sexual behaviors but felt they were simply consequences of his drinking and would go away when he sobered up. He was wrong. Holding both his addictions in check created enormous stress for John. He began to relieve that stress with prostitutes and heavy doses of pornography; soon they were an obsession.

John's wife knew about some of his behavior and threatened to leave him. He promised to stop but didn't. When he found he'd contracted a sexually transmitted disease, he went back to drinking rather than tell his wife.

Spending

Andrea had been chemically free for eight years and was active in Narcotics Anonymous. She was proud of the changes she had made during her recovery: completing her college degree, progressing in an exciting career, and making many new friends. Despite her success, she struggled with money. She earned a lot but spent more than she earned. Whenever she felt a little down, she went on a shopping spree, charging her credit cards to their limits. This felt good momentarily, but only until she had to pay the bills. Despite her considerable income, she borrowed money from relatives and friends, and took months to pay them back. Her constant borrowing eventually put a lot of pressure on her relationships with the friends who had lent her money. Some were angry because she didn't keep her word; others she avoided because of her embarrassment. Eventually she lost her home and had to file for bankruptcy. She never realized her spending was addictive.

Gambling

Dennis couldn't understand it. His wife left him, took the kids, and didn't bother to tell him where they were. *After all I've done for them!* he thought. *I stopped using drugs, just for them, and this is how they repay me.* It's true that Dennis had completed inpatient treatment one year earlier and stopped using cocaine and alcohol. But he never stopped gambling; he figured it wasn't a big deal. His wife and kids had long complained about his gambling and the ways it hurt the family, but he ignored them. He figured that by quitting drugs and alcohol, he had done all he needed to do. And anyway, why should he give up *all* his fun? But his bets with bookies and his purchase of lottery tickets put his family deep in debt and at times made money for food pretty scarce. Dennis felt he was entitled to a little fun; after all, he'd earned the money and had stopped using for his family's sake. What else could they possibly want?

Exercise

Carol's knee was throbbing as she lay in her hospital bed. *Why didn't I listen to my doctor?* she lamented as she was being prepared for surgery. Four months earlier, Carol's physician had warned her that if she continued to run daily, her knee would require surgery. Carol couldn't, or wouldn't, take his concerns seriously. After all, everything was going so well in her life. She had been sober for nine months, had regained her figure, and always felt wonderful after her daily routine of running seven to ten miles. She was rarely concerned about the aching and throbbing she often felt in her knee, nor was she bothered about all the time the running seemed to take away from her social life. All she knew was that she felt and looked good. She was, of course, depressed when she found out after surgery that she could never run again.

These stories all highlight the potential for addictive behavior by chemically dependent people. While sex, spending, gambling, and exercise are four of the most common behavior addictions, other noteworthy ones include food, risk-taking, and work. Addictive behavior can be described as any continuing activity that causes harm or problems in a person's life.

Why are some behaviors potentially addictive? This question deserves some explanation. Remember that we earlier discussed what chemically dependent people like to do most, which is "to feel good all the time." Their drug use allows them to feel good or escape, at least momentarily. Science now tells us something very interesting: we don't need to use drugs to take drugs. We are learning that certain behaviors alter our mood because they release powerful and pleasurable chemical reactions in our brains—natural drugs that are similar to sedatives, painkillers, and stimulants. This, by the way, is good. It's good for us to enjoy certain behaviors and the pleasurable feelings that may accompany them, but in moderation. For people prone to addictive behavior, however, the desire to feel good all the time often leads to repeating behaviors over and over again in order to release these natural mood-altering chemicals.

Addictive behaviors often start when the addict chooses to stop using chemicals. However, it's not uncommon for a behavioral addiction to precede the addict's drug use. But no matter when the behavior started, it needs to be acknowledged and treated. Behavioral addiction will always rob its victims of the quality of life they desire.

Some addictive behaviors can be addressed through complete abstinence. Others cannot. Gambling, for example, is a behavior that can be completely eliminated from an addict's life. But many other addictive behaviors can't be eliminated entirely. It would be impossible, for example, to "give up" eating or spending. Since abstinence just isn't an option in these areas, an addict must learn to set limits.

In some cases, these behavioral addictions can be treated through application of a Twelve Step program such as Alcoholics Anonymous (AA), Narcotics Anonymous (NA), or Cocaine Anonymous (CA). But often that won't work. In many cases, additional treatment is required to address behavioral addiction. Participation in a specialized Twelve Step group, such as Gamblers Anonymous, Sex Addicts Anonymous, and Overeaters Anonymous, becomes a vital addition to the recovery process for some. In other cases, the Twelve Step groups alone won't do the trick. In those instances, individual or group therapy directed by a trained counselor becomes a necessary step in recovery from addictive behaviors.

AT THE HEART OF THE PROBLEM:
A QUEST FOR WHOLENESS

Up to this point, we have examined many destructive ways the dependent person attempts to fill empty spaces in his or her life. Using mood-altering chemicals or addictive behaviors just won't work. What, then, is the answer? How can dependent people constructively satisfy their drive for wholeness?

A clue to the solution can be found by examining the thought of psychiatrist Carl Jung. Dr. Jung described the alcoholic's craving for alcohol as a spiritual quest for wholeness. This is an especially interesting insight for a psychiatrist to offer. Jung's experience supports the idea that the addict is driven by a sense of emptiness, or a void, that demands satisfaction. Particularly interesting, however, is that this world-renowned psychiatrist believed the addict's quest for wholeness is a spiritual problem that requires a spiritual solution. Jung suggested to Bill Wilson, cofounder of AA, that the void must be filled not with alcohol or other drugs, but with the satisfaction that comes through a relationship with God and supportive people. These relationships, according to Jung, will provide the strength needed to overcome addiction.

This is precisely what Twelve Step groups attempt to provide to their members: a healthy way to fill the void. The Twelve Steps themselves lead and direct individuals into a constructive, practical, and satisfying relationship with God, or a Higher Power. The fellowship of these groups provides intimate relationships with people and a sense of support, both of which allow members to feel hope, love, and acceptance. What results is the opportunity for a healthy and balanced new life. Maybe you should give one of these Twelve Step groups a try.

THE TWELVE STEPS OF ALCOHOLICS ANONYMOUS

1. We admitted we were powerless over alcohol—that our lives had become unmanageable.
2. Came to believe that a Power greater than ourselves could restore us to sanity.
3. Made a decision to turn our will and our lives over to the care of God *as we understood Him.*
4. Made a searching and fearless moral inventory of ourselves.
5. Admitted to God, to ourselves, and to another human being the exact nature of our wrongs.
6. Were entirely ready to have God remove all these defects of character.
7. Humbly asked Him to remove our shortcomings.
8. Made a list of all persons we had harmed, and became willing to make amends to them all.
9. Made direct amends to such people wherever possible, except when to do so would injure them or others.
10. Continued to take personal inventory and when we were wrong promptly admitted it.
11. Sought through prayer and meditation to improve our conscious contact with God *as we understood Him,* praying only for knowledge of His will for us and the power to carry that out.
12. Having had a spiritual awakening as the result of these steps, we tried to carry this message to alcoholics, and to practice these principles in all our affairs.

The Twelve Steps of AA are taken from *Alcoholics Anonymous,* 4th ed., published by AA World Services, Inc., New York, N.Y., 59–60.

About Hazelden Publishing

As part of the Hazelden Betty Ford Foundation, Hazelden Publishing offers both cutting-edge educational resources and inspirational books. Our print and digital works help guide individuals in treatment and recovery, and their loved ones. Professionals who work to prevent and treat addiction also turn to Hazelden Publishing for evidence-based curricula, digital content solutions, and videos for use in schools, treatment programs, correctional programs, and electronic health records systems. We also offer training for implementation of our curricula.

Through published and digital works, Hazelden Publishing extends the reach of healing and hope to individuals, families, and communities affected by addiction and related issues.

For more information about Hazelden publications,
please call **800-328-9000**
or visit us online at **hazelden.org/bookstore**.

Hazelden Classics for Continuing Care

For more than fifty years, Hazelden has been supporting people in the lifelong journey of recovery. The pamphlets in this series extend that offering of hope and guidance by exploring core issues that often arise in the later stages of recovery—issues that can tip the balance between continued growth and relapse.

Warding Off the Dangers of Cross-Addiction

True recovery requires making major lifestyle changes and, more important, finding a way to fill the void that led you to drug use in the first place. Until this happens, you are at high risk for relapse—to your drug of choice or to a new chemical or behavior. *A Look at Cross-Addiction* explains how recovering addicts can easily trade one addiction for another, how the denial involved can cause life to spin out of control, and how a Twelve Step program can help bring the wholeness that addicts seek.

Pamphlets in the Hazelden Classics for Continuing Care series

How to Get the Most Out of Group Therapy
Women and Relapse
Men's Issues in Recovery
A Look at Relapse
A Look at Cross-Addiction
Medication Use in Recovery

Hazelden
Publishing

hazelden.org/bookstore
800-328-9000

Order No. 5379

ISBN: 978-0-89486-331-8
90000

9 780894 863318